Payton's Little Prayers

COLORING BOOK

Payton's
Little Prayers
COLORING BOOK
Michaela A. Carter

To purchase books in bulk or for additional information, contact Mynd Matters Publishing
715 Peachtree Street NE
Suites 100 & 200
Atlanta, GA 30308
www.myndmatterspublishing.com

ISBN: 978-1-957092-69-0

FIRST EDITION

This Book Belongs to:

MY SPECIAL PRAYER

Printed in the USA
CPSIA information can be obtained
at www.ICGtesting.com
JSHW052030171023
50253JS00002B/12